CW00550389

THE
SALTIRE
SCOTTISH
SONG BOOK

Sixty Songs
for Unison or Solo Singing
with Piano

Edited by
CEDRIC THORPE DAVIE
and
GEORGE C. McVICAR

The Hardie Press

CONTENTS

The publisher acknowledges subsidy from
The Scottish Arts Council and Stirlingshire Educational Trust
towards the publication of this volume

© The Hardie Press, 1991

ISBN 0 946868 07 7

Originally published in 1969 by Oxford University Press
under the title 'The Oxford Scottish Song Book'

This edition published in Great Britain 1991 by
The Hardie Press, 17 Harrison Gardens, Edinburgh, EH11 1SE

Second Impression 1998

The purchase or hire of this work does not convey the right to perform it.
Permission to perform the work or material from the work in public must be
obtained from the Performing Right Society, 29/33 Berners Street, London
W1P 4AA, or its affiliates throughout the world, unless the owner or the
occupier of the premises being used holds a licence from the society.

All rights reserved. No part of this publication may be reproduced, stored in a
retrieval system, or transmitted, in any form or by any means, electronic,
mechanical, photocopying, recording or otherwise, without the prior
permission in writing from the publisher.

Printed in Great Britain by Martin's the Printers Ltd, Berwick upon Tweed

FOREWORD TO THE NEW EDITION

The presentation of Scottish traditional songs in arrangements for voice and keyboard has a long and distinguished history. Celebrated examples of the genre include William Thomson's *Orpheus Caledonius* (1725) and James Johnson's *Scots Musical Museum* (1787-1803). The line of descent has continued down to our own century, and 1969 saw the appearance of *The Oxford Scottish Song Book* hailed on publication as 'probably the best collection of Scots songs which has been produced in the last 50 years'.

Much has changed in Scottish life and culture since the publication of *The Oxford Scottish Song Book* including a reawakening to the individuality and poetic expressiveness of the lowland Scots tongue. A facet of the 'Oxford' edition providing for the 'substitution of suitable modifications of syllables or words' to enable the songs to 'be sung in English (as opposed to Scots)' is not a feature therefore of the new edition.

Appreciation of the musicianly arrangements of Cedric Thorpe Davie and George McVicar has not changed, however, and *The Saltire Scottish Song Book* (as the new edition is known) presents the opportunity to re-evaluate the very significant achievement of these two champions in the contemporary keyboard arrangements of the Scots song tradition.

THE PUBLISHERS,
EDINBURGH 1990.

PREFACE

The most difficult part of the making of this volume lay in selecting sixty songs from the enormous number that presented themselves. Inevitably the choice reflects to some extent the personal tastes of the editors, but they believe that the collection contains none but strong, characteristic melodies, covering the broadest possible range of emotions. Some of the songs are widely and deservedly popular; others are less well known, but are not for that reason any less worthy.

The collection contains material suitable for use by amateurs and professionals, by children, adults, and young people; the index shows the suitability of each song for solo use by men and women, and for class work in school. This classification is not claimed to be the final word on the subject; it does not extend to distinguishing between what is suitable for very young pupils and that which would appeal only to those at the top of the primary school. 'Wee Willie Gray', for example, will suit singers of all ages, from the very young to adults who can put over the song's delicate humour. On the other hand, the nostalgic 'The blue bell of Scotland' should not be attempted by children below the top stages of the primary school.

Many wonderful melodies were sorrowfully rejected because of the width of their compass; these included, for instance, 'The wauking of the fauld', 'On Ettrick's banks', and 'My tocher's the jewel'. Others are absent because they belong to a class or group for which space allowed only a limited representation; thus, the omission of 'Muirland Willie' is excusable only on the ground that 'The brisk young lad' is an even better example of its particular type. There will be criticism of the fact that the collection contains none of the Gaelic songs of the western isles. Nobody regrets this more than the editors, but despite their best efforts it proved impossible to provide translations from the Gaelic which were both singable and intelligible to the wider public at whom the volume is directed.

The singer's prime objective in these, as in all songs, must be to communicate the sense of the words to the listener; for this reason, few marks of expression are given, since interpretation of the meaning of the poem must bring with it varied expression between and within verses. Commas have been used to indicate the *maximum* number of breathing places, but the singer's phrasing must always be adapted to suit the verbal sense, and the accompanist's duty is to follow the phrasing of the singer. Minute alterations of time as between one verse and another are not only permissible, but essential where the accentuation of the words calls for it; the most common of these will be the interchange of ♪♩ and ♩♪. Singers must be guided in this matter by their musical and verbal sense, and should never plead the letter of the printed text as an excuse for a falsely accented word.

All the songs are capable of being effectively performed without accompaniment, and one or two are best given in this manner, as has been indicated by individual footnotes. In some cases there are varied accompaniments to one or more verses, but it is perfectly open to any singer or teacher to use the first-verse accompaniment throughout the song.

The given metronome speeds are guides; it should be remembered that what is right for one singer or for one room may be too fast or too slow for another. Middle keys have been chosen, but the songs may of course be sung in higher or lower keys.

C.T.D. AND G.C.M.
1969.

iv

NOTE ON THE TEXTS
AND PRONUNCIATION

The tunes. Most of the melodies exist in several slightly differing versions, in which small details have become altered in the course of generations of transmission from mouth to ear.

The editors have chosen the versions which seem to them most acceptable on grounds of pure melodic value; it is not suggested that these are necessarily more 'authentic' than any others, but they are no less so.

The words. The editors are grateful for advice freely given by Professor James Kinsley, one of the leading scholars in the field of Scottish verse, particularly that of Burns.

Careful comparison will reveal a few discrepancies between the words printed in this volume and the authentic texts in Burns's handwriting or the earliest printed sources, as established by Professor Kinsley. For these the editors take full responsibility, always bearing in mind that the volume is intended above all to be of practical use to singers. Such small variations are founded upon actual usage and custom, and have been introduced subconsciously in the past by singers in their endeavour to mark rhythm very clearly; they have become universally accepted for performance as if they were authentic. An example is the syllable 'o' which recurs frequently in the song 'Corn riggs'; this is not found in Burns's MS, but few will deny that it makes rhythmic performance of the song much easier. It may be noted that Burns himself, in songs such as 'My father was a farmer' did on occasion add single-vowel syllables of this kind, in order to fit his words neatly to the tune of his choice.

The pronunciation. It cannot be too strongly stated that no particular local dialect is to be preferred to another; Scottish singers should use the pronunciation which comes naturally to them, even where this seems to conflict with the spelling given in the text.

EDITORS' BIOGRAPHIES

CEDRIC THORPE DAVIE (1913-1983) studied in London with Ralph Vaughan Williams and in Budapest with Zoltan Kodaly. In 1945 he became Master of Music at the University of St. Andrews going on to hold the professorship there from 1973 until his retirement in 1978.

Apart from a large corpus of work for the cinema, theatre and radio, Thorpe Davie also wrote extensively in the genres of opera and operetta, orchestral, chamber, choral and vocal music. Many of his compositions were designed for performance by students, young people or amateurs often for specific forces at his disposal.

Cedric Thorpe Davie also found time to write on music: his work in this sphere includes articles, reviews for learned journals and the books *Musical Structure and Design* (1953) and *Scotland's Music* (1980).

GEORGE C. McVICAR has had a lifelong interest in folk-song and in particular that of his native Scotland. An early involvement with conducting choirs led him to publish some choral arrangements, but his first major contribution came with the invitation from Cedric Thorpe Davie to be joint-editor of *The Oxford Scottish Song Book*.

His professional career has been in musical education: first as a teacher, then as a lecturer at Moray House College of Education, and finally as music adviser to Stirlingshire and subsequently the Central Region. Other activities have included examining, adjudicating, music criticism and directing the Scottish Amateur Music Association's annual Summer School. Continuing interest in Scottish music is shown by his directing of the activities of the 'New Saltire Singers'.

He is also joint editor of *The New Scottish Song Book* (1987) and *The Saltire Two-Part Scottish Song Book* (1990).

1. CA THE YOWES

Words by Burns

C.T.D.

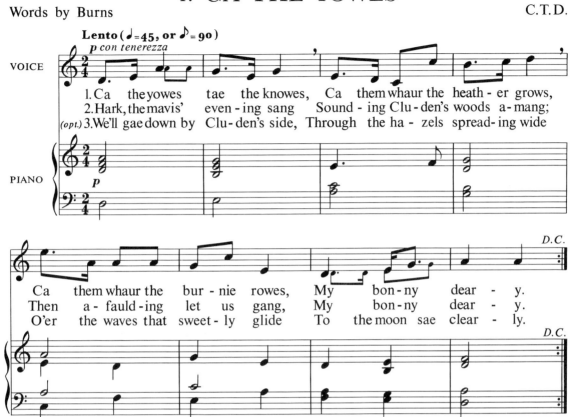

(Optional) 4. Ghaist nor bogle shalt thou fear,
Thou'rt to love and heav'n sae dear,
Nocht of ill may come thee near,
My bonny dearie.

5. Fair and lovely as thou art,
Thou hast stown my very heart;
I can die—but canna part,
My bonny dearie.

6. Ca the yowes tae the knowes,
Ca them where the heather grows,
Ca them where the burnie rowes,
My bonny dearie.

This song is best sung unaccompanied, but may be supported by simple chords as indicated. No elaboration of the pianoforte part should be attempted.

2. AE FOND KISS

Words by Burns

G.C.M.

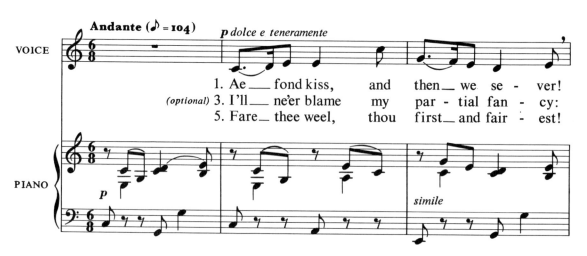

3. AIKEN DRUM

Words anonymous

G.C.M.

Con spirito (♩ = 84)

VOICE

mf

1. There__
2. An' his
3. An' his
4. But__

PIANO

f leggiero

mf

lived a man in__ oor toon, In oor toon, in
coat was o' the__ guid saut meat, The guid saut meat, the
ban-net was made o'__ pie - crust, O' pie - crust, o'
wae's me he turned__ so - ger, A so - ger, a

oor__ toon, There__ lived a man in__ oor toon, An' his
guid saut meat, An' a waist - coat o'__ the__ hag - gis bag_____
pie - crust, An' his ban-net was made o'__ pie - crust_____
so - ger, But__ wae's me he turned__ so - ger, An'

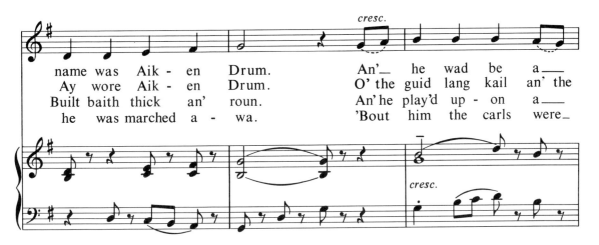

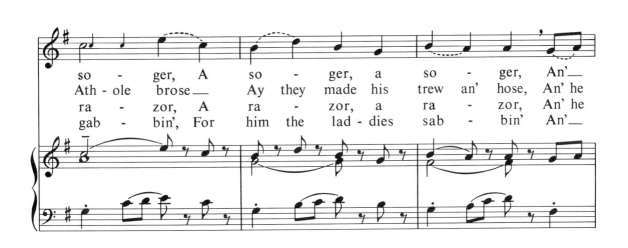

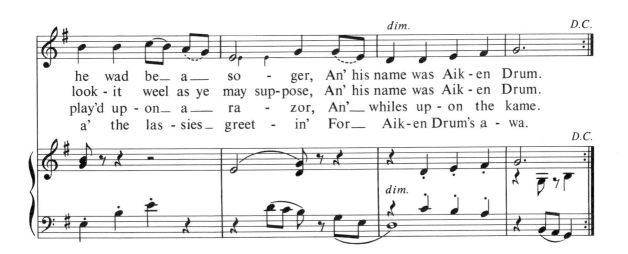

4. BY YON CASTLE WA

Words by Burns

C.T.D.

(4.) life is a bur - den that bows___ me___ down, Since___ I tint___ my___ bairns___ and he tint his___ crown; But___ till___ my___ last___ mo - ments my words are the same; There'll ne - ver___ be___ peace___ till Ja - mie comes___ hame.'___

5. BONNY WEE THING

Words by Burns

C.T.D.

Bon - ny— wee— thing, can - ny— wee— thing,

Love -ly— wee— thing, was thou— mine I— would— wear— thee

in— my— bo - som, Lest— my— jew - el I should tine.

1. Wist - ful - ly— I— look— and— lan - guish In that bon - ny—

2. Wit and grace— and— love— and— beau - ty In ae con - stel -

face o'— thine,— And my heart— it stounds wi an-guish—
-la—tion— shine,— To a-dore— thee is— my du-ty,—

Lest— my— wee— thing be na— mine.
God-dess— o' — this soul o' — mine!

Bon - ny— wee— thing,
can - ny— wee— thing, Love-ly— wee— thing, was thou— mine

I— would— wear thee in— my— bo - som Lest my— jew- el I should— tine.

con ped.

6. AY WAUKIN O

Words by Burns

G.C.M.

7. IN YON GARDEN FINE AN' GAY

Words anonymous

G.C.M.

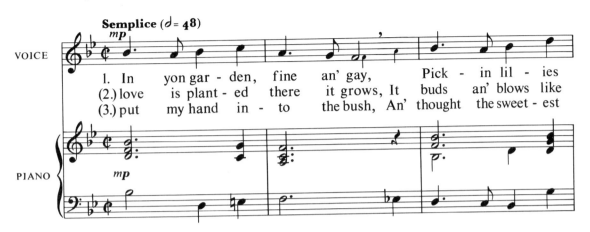

1. In yon gar - den, fine an' gay, Pick - in lil - ies
(2.) love is plant - ed there it grows, It buds an' blows like
(3.) put my hand in - to the bush, An' thought the sweet - est

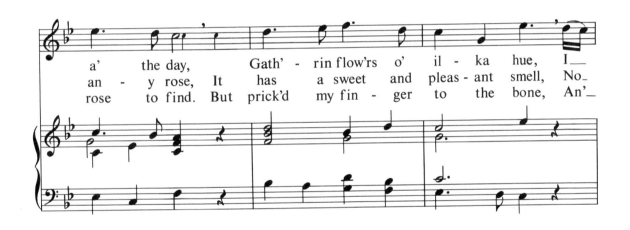

a' the day, Gath' - rin flow'rs o' il - ka hue, I
an - y rose, It has a sweet and pleas - ant smell, No
rose to find. But prick'd my fin - ger to the bone, An'

Verses 1 - 2   D.C. | Verse 3

wist na' then what love could do.   2. Where
flow'r on earth can it ex - cel.   3. I
left the sweet - est   rose be - hind.

8. CORN RIGGS

Words by Burns

G.C.M.

Allegro moderato (♩=80)

1. It was up-on a Lam-mas nicht, When corn riggs are bon-ny o, Be-neath the moon's un-cloud-ed licht, I held a wa to An-nie o. The time fled by wi tent-less heed, Till
2. The sky was blue, the wind was still, The moon was shin-ing clear-ly o, I set her doon wi richt guid-will, A-mang the riggs o' bar-ley o. I kent her hairt was a' my ain, I
3. I lock'd her in my fond em-brace, Her heart was beat-ing rare-ly o, My bless-ings on that hap-py place, A-mang the riggs o' bar-ley o. But by the moon and stars sae bricht, That

tween the late_ an'_ ear - ly - o, Wi sma per - sua - sion_
lo'd her maist_ sin - cere - ly - o, I kiss'd her owr_ an'_
shone that hour_ sae _ clear - ly - o, She aye shall bless_ that_

she _ a - greed To see_ me_ thro'_the_ bar - ley - o.
owr_ a - gain, A - mang_the_ riggs_o'_ bar - ley - o.
hap - py _nicht, A - mang_the_ riggs_o'_ bar - ley - o.

Corn_ riggs_and_ bar - ley_riggs, And corn_ riggs_are_ bon - ny - o, I'll

p staccato

D.C.

ne'er for - get_that_ hap - py_nicht, A - mang_the_riggs_wi'_ An - nie - o.

D.C.

4. I hae been blythe wi comrades dear;
        I hae been merry drinking-o;
    I hae been joyfu gathrin gear;
        I hae been happy thinking-o:
    But a' the pleasures e'er I saw,
        Tho three times doubl'd fairly-o,
    That happy night was worth them a',
        Amang the riggs o' barley-o.

9. DUNCAN GRAY

Words by Burns

G.C.M.

4. How it comes let doc-tors tell, Ha, ha, the woo - in o't,
5. Dun-can was a lad o' grace, Ha, ha, the woo - in o't,

Meg grew sick as he grew hale, Ha, ha, the woo-in o't,
Mag - gie's was a pit - eous case, Ha, ha, the woo-in o't,

Some-thing in her_ bo-som wrings, For re - lief a sigh she brings, An'
Dun-can could-na_ be her death, Swell-ing pi - ty smoor'd his wrath,

oh, her_ een they spak_ sic_things, Ha, ha, the woo-in o't.
Noo they're crouse an' can - ty_baith, Ha, ha, the woo-in o't.

10. FLOW GENTLY, SWEET AFTON

Words by Burns

C.T.D.

after verse 4
only. Omit this
bar before
verse 3.

3. How plea-sant thy_ banks and green_ vall-eys be - low,_ Where wild in the_ wood-lands the_ prim - ros - es_ blow; There_ oft, as_ mild_ even-ing weeps o - ver the_ lea,_ The sweet scent-ed_ birk_shades my_ Ma - ry_ and_ me._

11. I HAE LAID A HERRIN IN SAUT

Words by James Tytler

C.T.D.

1. I hae laid a herrin in saut, Lass, gin ye loe me, tell me noo, I hae brewed a forpit o maut, And I canna come ilka
2. I hae a hoose on yonder moor, Lass, gin ye loe me, tell me noo, Three sparrows may dance upon the floor, And I canna come ilka
3. I hae a hen wi a happity leg, Lass, gin ye loe me, tell me noo, That ilka day lays me an egg, And I canna come ilka

day_ to woo; I hae a calf that will soon be a coo,
day_ to woo; I hae a but_ and I hae a ben,
day_ to woo; I hae a keb-bock up - on_ my shelf,

Lass gin ye loe_ me, tell_ me noo,____ I hae a pig that will
Lass gin ye loe_ me, tell_ me noo,_ A pen- ny to keep and a
Lass gin ye loe_ me, tell_ me noo,_ I can - na eat it

soon be a soo, And I can-na come il - ka day_ to woo.
pen- ny to spen, And I can-na come il - ka day_ to woo.
a'___ my-self, And I can-na come il - ka day_ to woo.

D.C.
(last verse)

12. I'LL AY CA IN BY YON TOUN

Words by Burns

C.T.D.

13. JOHNNIE COPE

Words by Adam Skirving

G.C.M.

14. JOCKY SAID TO JENNY

Words anonymous
(before 1700)

C.T.D.

1. Jock-y said to Jen-ny, 'Jen-ny, wilt thou do't?'
2. 'I hae gowd and gear,— I hae land e-neugh,
3. 'I hae a guid house, a barn— and a— byre, A
4. Jen-ny said to Jock-y, 'Gin ye win-na— tell,

'Ne'er a fit,' quo Jen-ny, 'for my— toch-er good,
I hae sax guid ox-en gang-ing— in a pleugh,
stack be-fore the door will mak a — ran-tin fire,
Ye shall be the lad, I'll be the— lass my-sel;

For my toch-er good I win-na mar-ry— thee.'
Gang-ing in— a— pleugh and link-ing owre the— lea,
Mak a ran-tin— fire, and mer-ry we— will be, But
Ye're a bon-ny— lad and I'm a las-sie— free, Ye're

'Een's ye like,'— quo— Jock-y, 'Ye can— let me be.
Gin ye win-na— tak me I can— let ye be.
gin ye win-na— tak me I can— let ye be.'
wel-com-er— to— tak me than to— let me be.'

15. IT WAS A' FOR OUR RIGHTFU KING

Words by Burns

C.T.D.

16. JOHN ANDERSON MY JO

Words by Burns

G.C.M.

1. John_ An-der-son my jo, John, When_ we were first ac-
2. John_ An-der-son my jo, John, We_ clamb the hill the-

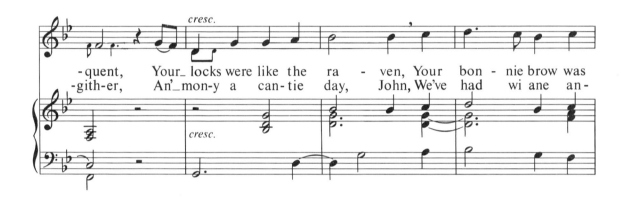

-quent, Your_ locks were like the ra - ven, Your bon - nie brow was
-gith-er, An'_ mon-y a can-tie day, John, We've had wi ane an-

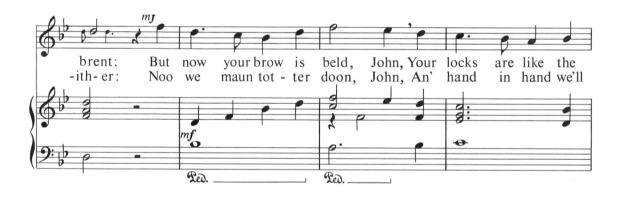

brent; But now your brow is beld, John, Your locks are like the
-ith-er: Noo we maun tot - ter doon, John, An' hand in hand we'll

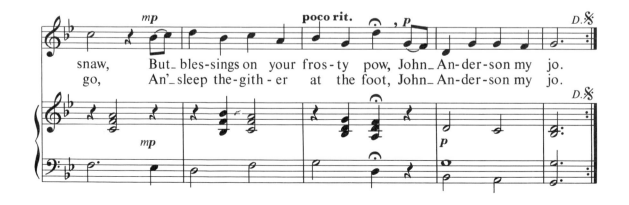

snaw, But_ bles-sings on your fros-ty pow, John_ An-der-son my jo.
go, An'_ sleep the-gith - er at the foot, John_ An-der-son my jo.

17. O WILLY'S RARE AND WILLY'S FAIR

Words anonymous

C.T.D.

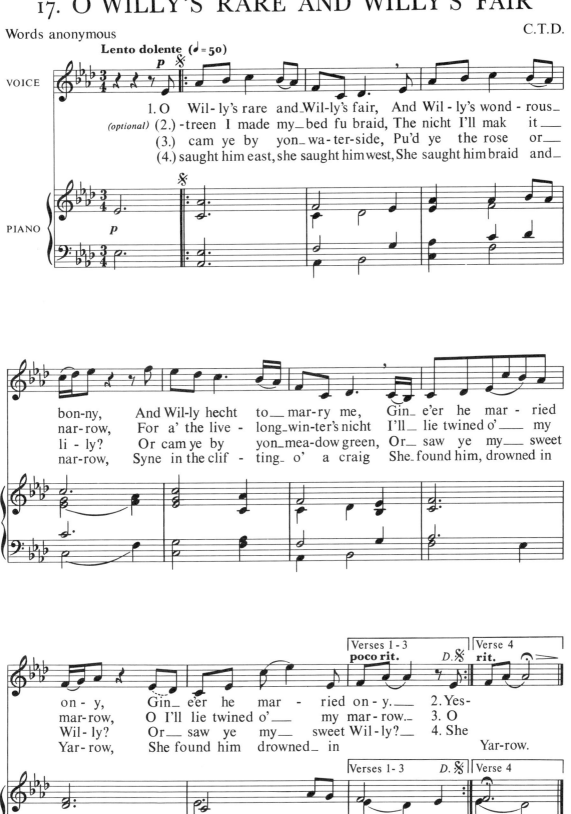

18. JOHNNY FAA

Words anonymous

C.T.D.

Lento (♩=48)

VOICE

PIANO

con ped.

1. The gip - sies— cam tae our— lord's yett, And
2. 'Sae tak frae— me this gay— man - tle, And
3. 'Come tae your bed,' says John - ny— Faa,——
4. 'I'll mak a— hap tae my John - ny— Faa, I'll

oh! but they— sang bon - ny, They sang sae sweet and sae— com-plete That
bring tae me— a— plai - die, For if kith and kin and a'— had— sworn, I'll
'come tae your bed, my— dear - y, For I vow and swear by the hilt o' my sword, Your
mak a hap tae my dear - y, And he'll get a' that it— gaes round, And my

doon cam oor— fair— la - dy; When she cam trip - ping doon the— stair And
fol - low the gyp-sy— lad - dy; Yest-reen I— lay in a weel-made-bed, And
lord shall nae mair— come— near ye.' 'I'll go tae bed tae my John - ny— Faa, And I'll
lord shall nae mair— come— near me.' And when our lord cam hame at— e'en, And

a' her maids be - fore her, As soon as they saw her weel-faured face, They—
my guid lord be - side me; This nicht I'll— lie in a ten - ant's barn, What-
go tae bed tae my dear - y, For I vow and swear by what passed yest-reen, My—
speired for his fair la - dy, The tane she— cried, and the i - ther re-plied, 'She's a-

19 KIND ROBIN LOES ME

Words anonymous

C.T.D.

20. KELVINGROVE

Words by Thomas Lyle

G.C.M.

21. THE BOB O' DUNBLANE

Words anonymous

G.C.M.

Energico (♩.=72)

VOICE

PIANO

1. Come, las-sie, lend me___ your braw___ hemp he-ckle, An'
2. Haste___ ye gang to the ground o' yer trun - kies,
3. Be frank,___ my las-sie, lest I___ grow fi-ckle, An'
4. The din-ner, the pi - per and priest sall be read-y, An'

I'll___ lend you___ my thrip - ling kame; For fain - ness, dea - ry, I'll
Busk ye braw___ an' din - na think shame: Con - si - der in time,___ if
take___ my word___ an' of - fer a - gain. Syne ye___ may chance to re-
I'm___ grown do - wy___ wi ly - ing my lane: A - way___ then, leave___ baith

gar___ ye ke-ckle, If ye'll___ gae dance___ the Bob o' Dun-blane.
lead-ing of mon-kies Be bet-ter than danc-ing the Bob o' Dun-blane.
-pent___ it mi-ckle, Ye did-nae ac-cept o' the Bob o' Dun-blane.
min-ny an' dad-dy, An' try___ wi me___ the Bob o' Dun-blane.

D.C.

22. LADY ANNE BOTHWELL'S LAMENT

Words anonymous

C.T.D.

23. MAGGIE LAUDER

Words by Francis Sempill

C.T.D.

VOICE / PIANO — Allegro ritmico (♩=120)

1. Wha wad - na be in love Wi
(2.) -gie" quo he, "and by my bags I'm
(3.) -er," quo Meg; "hae ye your bags, And

bon - nie Mag - gie Lau - der? A pip - er met her gaun to Fife, And
fid - gin fain tae see ye; Sit down by me, my bon - ny bird, In
is your drone in or - der? If ye be Rob, I've heard o' ye, Live

spierd what was't they ca'd her; Richt scorn-ful - ly she an-swered him, "Be-
troth I win - na steer thee; For I'm a pi - per to my trade, My
ye up - on the bor - der? The las - sies a', baith far and near, Hae

-gone, ye hal - lan - sha - ker, Jog on your gate, ye bla - ther - skate, My
name is Rob the Ran - ter: The las - sies loup as they were daft When
heard o' Rob the Ran - ter: I'll shake my foot wi richt guid-will Gif

Verses 1 – 4

name is Mag - gie   Lau - der."
I   blaw up   my   chan - ter."
ye'll blaw up your   chan - ter."

2. "Mag-
3. "Pip-
4. Then

Verse 5

5. Lau - der!

4. Then to his bags he flew wi speed
        About the drone he twisted;
    Meg up and walloped ower the green,
        For brawley could she frisk it!
    "Weel done!" quo he. "Play up," quo she.
        "Weel bobbed," quo Rob the Ranter,
    "It's worth my while to play, indeed,
        When I hae sic a dancer."

5. "Weel hae ye played your part," quo Meg,
        "Your cheeks are like the crimson,
    There's nane in Scotland plays sae weel
        Since we lost Habbie Simson;
    I've lived in Fife, baith maid and wife
        This ten years and a quarter:
    Gin ye should come to Anster Fair,
        Spier ye for Maggie Lauder."

24. LAMENT OF THE BORDER WIDOW

Words anonymous

C.T.D.

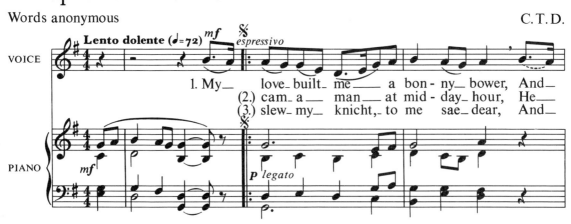

This song is best sung without accompaniment

4. I sew'd his sheet and made my maen;
(Opt.) I watch'd his corpse mysel alane;
I watch'd by nicht and I watch'd by day,
Nae living creature cam my way.

5. I bore his body on my back
And whiles I went, and whiles I sat;
I digg'd a grave and laid him in,
And happ'd him wi the sod sae green.

6. But think na ye my heart was sair,
(Opt.) When I laid the moul on his yellow hair?
Oh, think na ye my heart was wae
When I turned about, away to gae?

7. The man lives not I'll love again
Since that my comely knicht is slain.
Wi ae lock o' his yellow hair
I'll bind my heart for evermair.

25. MY BOY TAMMIE

Words by Hector Macneill

G.C.M.

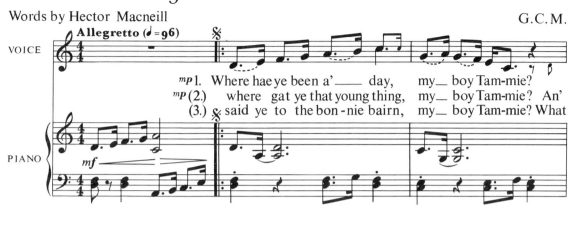

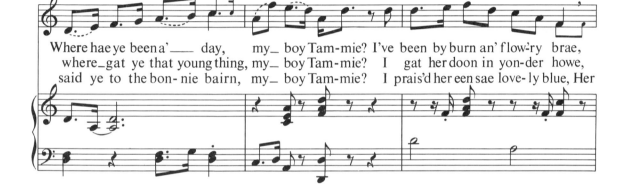

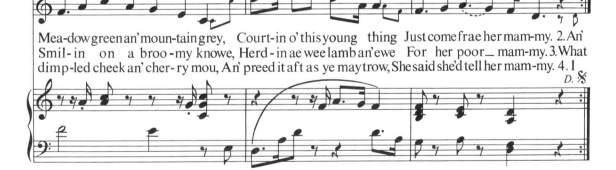

4. I held her to my beatin heart,
   My young, my smilin lammie.
   'I hae a house, it cost me dear,
   I've wealth o' plenishin an' gear.
   Ye'll get it a' wer't ten times mair,
   Gin ye'll leave your mammie.'

5. 'Has she been to kirk wi thee,
   My boy Tammie?'
   'She has been to kirk wi me,
   An' the tear was in her ee,
   For O! she's but a young thing,
   Just come frae her mammie.'

26. MY LOVE SHE'S BUT A LASSIE YET

Words by Burns

G.C.M.

love she's but a las-sie yet, My love she's but a las-sie yet, We'll let her stand a year or twa, She'll no be half sae sau-cy yet.

1. I rue the day I sought her o! I rue the day I sought her o! Wha gets her needs na say he's woo'd, But he may say he's bought her o!

2. Come draw a drap o' the best o't yet, Come draw a drap o' the best o't yet, Gae seek for plea-sure where ye will, But here I ne-ver miss'd it yet.

My

love she's but a las-sie yet, My love she's but a las-sie yet, We'll let her stand a

year or twa, She'll no be half sae sau-cy yet. We're a' a-dry wi drink-in o't, We're

a' a-dry wi drink-in o't, The mi-ni-ster kiss'd the fidd-ler's wife, He

could-na preach for think-in o't. My love she's but a las-sie yet, My love she's but a

las-sie yet, We'll let her stand a year or twa, She'll no be half sae sau-cy yet.

27. MY LOVE'S IN GERMANY

Words by Hector Macneill

C.T.D.

1. My love's in Ger-ma-ny, send him hame, send him hame, My love's in Ger-ma-ny,— send him hame.— My— love's in Ger-ma-ny Fecht-in brave for roy-al-ty, He may ne'er his Jea-nie see,— send him hame, send him hame, He may ne'er his Jea-nie see,— send him hame. 2. He's

3. Our faes are ten to three, send him hame, send him hame, Our— faes are ten to three, send him hame.— Our— faes are ten to three, He maun ei-ther fa or flee, In the cause o' loy-al-ty,— send him hame, send him hame, In the cause o' loy-al-ty,— send him hame. 4. He'll

28. O CAN YE SEW CUSHIONS?

Words anonymous

C.T.D.

29. THE FLOWERS O' THE FOREST

Words by Jean Elliot

C.T.D.

This song is best sung without accompaniment.

30. NOW NATURE HANGS HER MANTLE GREEN

(Lament of Mary, Queen of Scots)

Words by Burns

G.C.M.

5. The mean - est hind in fair Scot - land May rove their sweets a - mang; But I, the Queen of a' Scot - land, Maun lie in pri - son strang.

31. O GIN I WERE A BARON'S HEIR

Words anonymous

G.C.M.

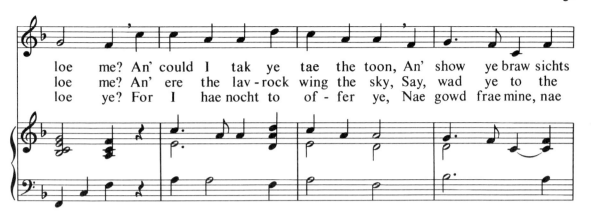

loe me? An' could I tak ye tae the toon, An' show ye braw sichts
loe me? An' ere the lav-rock wing the sky, Say, wad ye to the
loe ye? For I hae nocht to of - fer ye, Nae gowd frae mine, nae

mony an ane, An' busk ye fine in silk - en goon,___
for - est hie, An' work wi me sae mer - ri - ly?___
pearl frae sea, Nor am I come o' high de - gree,___

Verses 1 – 2   D.S.   Verse 3

Las-sie, wad ye loe me?   2. Or
Las-sie, wad ye loe me?   3. An'
Las-sie, but I   loe ye.

32. O GIN I WERE WHERE GADIE RINS

Words by John Imlah

G.C.M.

Ga- die rins, where Ga- die rins, where Ga- die rins,_ O_ gin I_ were where

Ga - die rins, By the foot o' Ben- a - chie.

1. I've roam'd by Tweed, I've
2. When blade an' blos - soms
3. When sim - mer cleads the

roam'd by Tay, By_ bor - der Nith an' High - land_ Spey,_ But_
sprout in spring, An'_ bid the bird - ies wag_ the_ wing,_ They_
var - ied scene Wi licht o' gowd an' leaves_ o'_ green, I_

dear-er far to me than they Are the braes o' Ben- a - chie.
blith-ly bob an' soar an' sing By the foot o' Ben- a - chie.
fain wad be where aft I've been, At the foot o' Ben- a - chie.

O—

gin I— were where— Ga-die rins, where Ga-die rins, where— Ga-die rins,— O—

gin I—were where— Ga - die rins, By the foot o' Ben-a - chie.

4. When autumn's yellow sheaf is shorn,
   An' barnyards stored wi stooks o' corn,
   'Tis blithe to toom the clyack horn
   At the foot o' Benachie.
      O gin I were etc. . .

5. When winter winds blaw sharp an' shrill
   O'er icy burn an' sheeted hill,
   The ingle neuk is gleesome still
   At the foot o' Benachie.

33. O KENMURE'S ON AND AWA, WILLIE

Words by Burns

C.T.D.

-ess   to   Ken - mure's   band._____   There's   no   a   heart_   that
Ken - mure's   lads_   are   men!_____   Their   hearts   and   swords_   are
him   that's   far___   a - wa!_____   And   here's   the   flower_   that

fears_   a   whig___   That   rides   by   Ken - mure's   hand._____
met - al   true,_   And   that   their   faes_   shall   ken._____
I___   loe   best:_   The   rose   that's   like_   the

Verses 1 - 2

D. 𝄋 | Last verse

2. Here's
3. They'll

snaw._____

34. O LAY THY LOOF IN MINE, LASS

Words by Burns

G.C.M.

less thou'lt be my ain. O (2.)-e - ver to re-main.

O lay thy loof in mine, lass, in

mine, lass, in mine,— lass, An' swear on thy white hand, lass, That

thou wilt be my ain.

35. O GIN MY LOVE WERE YON RED ROSE

Words:
v. 1 & refrain anonymous
vv. 2 - 3 by Burns

C.T.D.

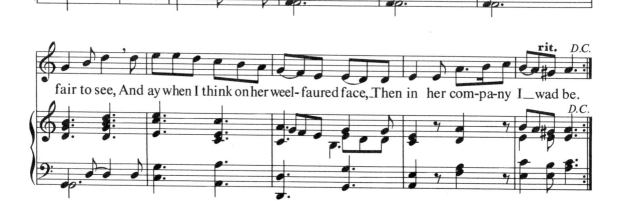

36. O THIS IS NO' MY AIN LASSIE

Words by Burns

G.C.M.

O this is no' my ain lassie, Fair tho the

las-sie be: O weel ken I my ain lassie— Kind love is in her ee.

1. I see a form, I see a face, Ye weel may wi the fair-est place: It
2. She's bon-nie, bloom-ing, straight and tall, And lang has had my heart in thrall; And
3. A thief sae paw-kie is my Jean, To steal a blink by a' un-seen! But
4. It may es-cape the court-ly sparks, It may es-cape the learn-ed clerks: But

wants to me the witch-ing grace, The kind love that's in her ee. O
ay it charms my ver-y saul, The kind love that's in her ee. O
gleg as licht are lov-ers' een, When kind love is in the ee. O
well the watch-ing lov-er marks The kind love that's in her ee. O

37. RATTLIN ROARIN WILLIE

Words:
vv. 1&2 anonymous
v. 3 by Burns

C.T.D.

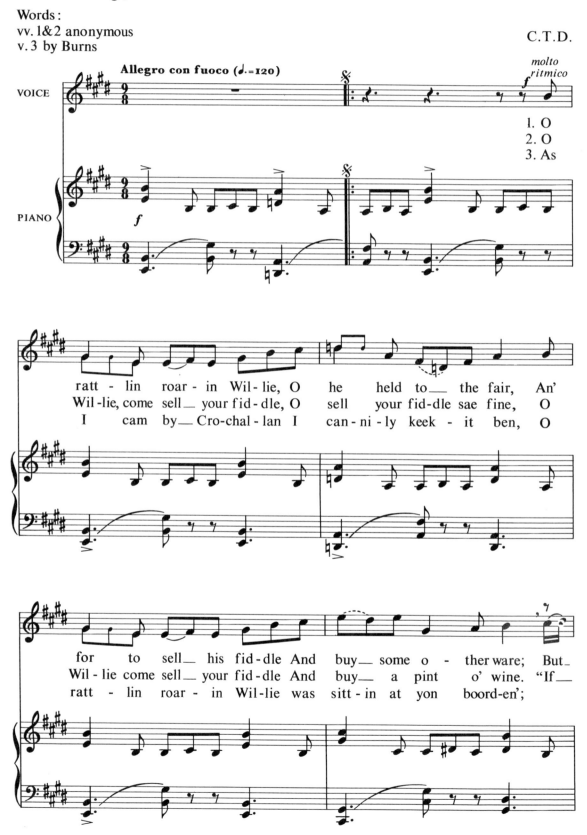

38. THE BIRKS OF ABERFELDY

Words by Burns

C.T.D.

Bon-ny las-sie, will ye go,—Will ye go, will ye go, Bon-ny las-sie, will ye go To the

birks of A-ber-fel - - dy?

1. Now sim-mer blinks on flower-y braes, And
2. The lit-tle bird-ies blithe-ly sing, While
3. The braes as-cend like lof-ty wa's, The
4. Let for-tune's gifts at ran-dom flee, They

o'er the cry-stal stream-lets plays, Come, let us spend the light-some days In the
o'er their heads the ha-zels hing, Or light-ly flit on wan-ton wing In the
foam-y stream deep roar-ing fa's, O'er-hung wi fra-grant spread-ing shaws, The
ne'er shall draw a wish frae me, Su-preme-ly blest wi love and thee In the

birks of A-ber-fel - dy.
birks of A-ber-fel - dy.
birks of A-ber-fel - dy.
birks of A-ber-fel - dy.

Bon-ny las-sie, will ye go,—Will ye go,—will ye go,—

Bon-ny las-sie, will ye go To the birks of A-ber-fel - dy? birks of A-ber-fel - dy?

39. WEE WILLIE GRAY

Words by Burns

G.C.M.

1. Wee Wil-lie Gray and his lea-ther wal-let,
2. Wee Wil-lie Gray and his lea-ther wal-let,

Peel a wil-lie wand to be him boots an' ja-cket: Rose up-on the briar will
Twice a li-ly-flow'r will be him sark an' cra-vat: Fea-thers of a flee wad

be him trouse an' doub-let, Rose up-on the briar will be him trouse an' doub-let!
fea-ther up his bon-net, Fea-thers of a flee wad fea-ther up his bon-net!

40. O WEEL MAY THE BOATIE ROW

Words by John Ewen

C.T.D.

1. O weel__ may the boat-ie row, And bet-ter may she speed, And lee-some may the boat-ie row That wins the bairns__ bread. The boat-ie rows, the boat-ie rows, The boat-ie rows in-deed, And__ weel__ may__the boat-ie__row That

(2.) cast my line in Lar-go bay, And fish-es I catched nine, There was three to boil, and three to fry, And three to bait__ the line. The boat-ie rows, the boat-ie rows, The boat-ie rows in-deed, And__ hap-py be__ the lot o'__ a' Who

(3.) weel__ may the boat-ie row That fills a heav-y creel, And cleads us a' frae head to feet, And buys our parr-itch meal. The boat-ie rows, the boat-ie rows, The boat-ie rows in-deed, And__ hap-py be__ the lot o'__ a' Who

(4.) Saw-ney,Jock an' Jan-et-ty Are up and got-ten lear, They'll help to gar the boat-ie row And licht-en a'__ our care. The boat-ie rows, the boat-ie rows, The boat-ie rows fu weel, And__ light-some be__ her heart that_bears The

wins my bairns bread.)
wish-es her to speed.
wish-es her to speed.
mur-lain and the creel.)

O weel— may the boat-ie row And

bet-ter may she speed, And lee-some may the boat-ie row That

all verses except last

D. %

wins my bairns— bread.—

2. I
3. O
4. When

D. %

all verses except last

last verse **rit.**

wins my bairns— bread.—

last verse **rit.**

41. O WHISTLE AND I'LL COME TO YE, MY LAD

Words by Burns

G.C.M.

1. But _ war - i - ly tent when ye come to court me, And come nae un - less the back
2. At _ kirk or at mar-ket when-e'er ye meet me, Gang _ by me as tho that ye
3. Ay _ vow and pro-test that ye care na for me, And whiles ye may licht-ly my

yett be a - jee: Syne _ up the back style and let nae-bod-y see, And _
cared nae a flee: But _ steal me a blink o' your bon-nie black ee, Yet _
beau-ty a wee: But _ court nae an - ith - er tho jok-in ye be, For _

come as ye were _ na com-in to me, An' _ come as ye were _ na com-in to me.
look as ye were _ na look-in at me. Yet _ look as ye were _ na look-in at me.
fear that she wile your fan-cy frae me, For _ fear that she wile your fan-cy frae me.

42. O WILLIE WAS A WANTON WAG

Words attributed to
William Hamilton

G.C.M.

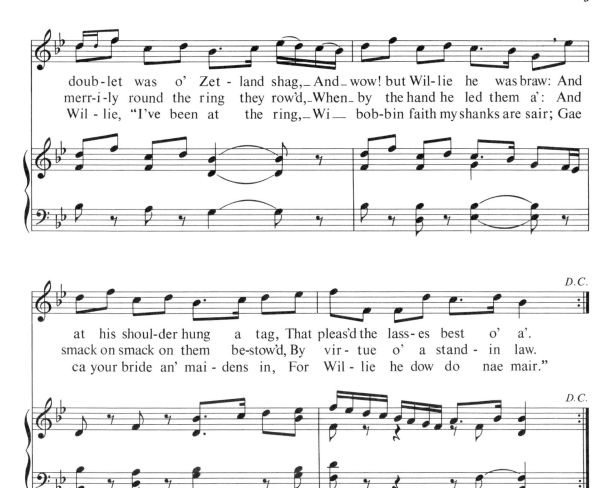

doub-let was o' Zet - land shag,_ And_ wow! but Wil-lie he was braw: And
merr-i-ly round the ring they row'd,_ When_ by the hand he led them a': And
Wil - lie, "I've been at the ring,_ Wi_ bob-bin faith my shanks are sair; Gae

at his shoul-der hung a tag, That pleas'd the lass-es best o' a'.
smack on smack on them be-stow'd, By vir - tue o' a stand - in law.
ca your bride an' mai - dens in, For Wil - lie he dow do nae mair."

4.   Then rest ye, Willie, I'll gae out
        An' for a wee fill up the ring;
But shame light on his supple snout,
        He wanted Willie's wanton fling.
Then straight he to the bride did fare,
        Says, "Weel's me on your bonnie face:
Wi bobbin Willie's shanks are sair
        An' I'm come out to fill his place."

5.   "Bridegroom", says she, "you'll spoil the dance,
        An' at the ring you'll aye be lag,
Unless like Willie you advance,
        O Willie has a wanton leg.
For wit he learns us a' to steer
        An' foremost aye bears up the ring:
We will find nae sic dancing here,
        If we want Willie's wanton fling."

43. TAM GLEN

Words by Burns

C.T.D.

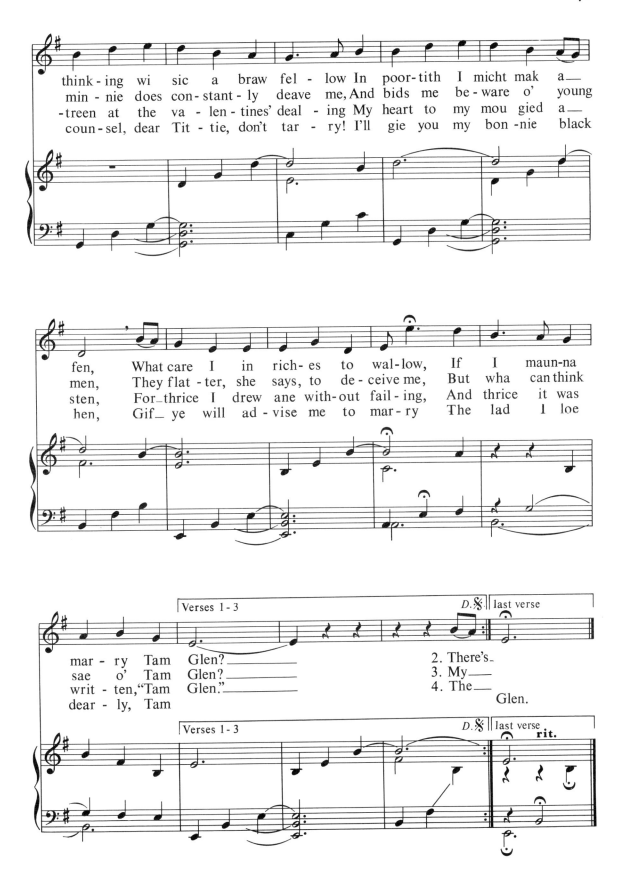

thinking wi sic a braw fel - low In poor-tith I micht mak a —
min - nie does con - stant - ly deave me, And bids me be - ware o' young
-treen at the va - len - tines' deal - ing My heart to my mou gied a —
coun - sel, dear Tit - tie, don't tar - ry! I'll gie you my bon - nie black

fen, What care I in rich - es to wal - low, If I maun-na
men, They flat - ter, she says, to de - ceive me, But wha can think
sten, For_thrice I drew ane with-out fail - ing, And thrice it was
hen, Gif_ ye will ad - vise me to mar - ry The lad I loe

| Verses 1 - 3 | | | D.%. | last verse |

mar - ry Tam Glen?_____ 2. There's_
sae o' Tam Glen?_____ 3. My___
writ - ten, "Tam Glen."_____ 4. The___
dear - ly, Tam Glen.

| Verses 1 - 3 | | | D.%. | last verse rit. |

44. THE AULD MAN'S MARE'S DEID

Words by Patie Birnie

C.T.D.

auld man's mare's deid A mile a-bune Dun-dee. 2. There was hay to ca and lint to lead, A

3. She had the cleeks, the cauld, the crooks, The

4. She had the fier-cie and the fleuk, The

hun-ner hotts o' muck to spread, And peats and truffs and a' to lead, And

jaw-pish and the dun-ner-peuks, Her lun-zie-banes were knags and neuks, And

wheez-lock and the wan-ton yeuk, On il-ka knee she had a breuk, What

yet the jaud to dee.

howks a-bune her ee.

ail'd the brute to dee?

The auld man's mare's deid, The

puir man's mare's deid, The auld man's mare's deid A mile a-bune Dun-dee.

45. THE BLUE BELL OF SCOTLAND

Words by Anne Grant

G.C.M.

46. THE QUEEN'S MARIES

Words anonymous

G.C.M.

47. THE BONNY BANKS OF LOCH LOMOND

Words anonymous

C.T.D.

1. By yon bon-ny banks and by yon bon-ny braes, Where the
2. I mind where we part-ed in yon sha-dy glen, On the
3. The wee bird-ies sing and the wild flow-ers spring, And in

sun shines bright on Loch Lo - mond, There me and my true love spent
steep, steep side o' Ben Lo - mond, Where in deep pur-ple hue the
sun-shine the wat-ers are sleep - ing, But the brok-en hert will

mo-ny hap-py days   On the bon-ny, bon-ny banks o' Loch Lo - mond.
High-land hills we view,   And the moon shines out in the gloam - ing. Oh,
ken nae se-cond spring Though the wae - fu should cease frae their greet - ing.

ye'll tak the high road And I'll tak the low road, And I'll be in Scot - land be-

- fore ye, But wae is my hert un - til we meet a - gain On the
alternative [But me and my true love will ne -ver meet a -gain]

bon- ny, bon-ny banks o' Loch Lo - - mond.

This song may very well be sung without accompaniment.

48. THE BRISK YOUNG LAD

Words anonymous

C.T.D.

brisk   young lad and a   braw_ young lad,_ And wow!   but he was a braw_young lad_ Cam seek - ing me_ to woo!_____ woo!

Verses 1 - 6   D.S   last verse

4. "Gae, get you gone, you cauldrife wooer,
Ye soor-looking cauldrife wooer!"
I straightway showed him to the door
Saying, "Come nae mair to woo."
And wow! etc.

5. There lay a deuk-dub before the door,
Before the door, before the door,
There lay a deuk-dub before the door
And there he fell, I trow.
And wow! etc.

6. Out cam the guidman and high he shouted,
Out cam the guidwife and laigh she looted,
And a' the town neighbours were gathered aboot it
And there lay he, I trow.
And wow! etc.

7. Then out cam I and sneered and smiled,
"Ye cam to woo, but ye're a' beguiled,
Ye've faun i' the dirt and ye're a' befyled,
We'll hae nae mair o' you."
And wow! etc.

49. THE BROOM O' THE COWDENKNOWES

Words anonymous

G.C.M.

1. How blithe was I ilk morn to see My swain come o'er the hill. He leap'd the burn and flew to me; I met him wi good will.
2. I neither wanted ewe nor lamb, While his flock near me lay; He ga-ther'd in my sheep at night, And cheer'd me a' the day.
3. He tun'd his pipe and reed sae sweet, The birds stood list'-ning by; E'en the dull cat-tle stood and gazed, Charm'd wi his mel-od-y.
4. While thus we spent our time by turns, Be-twist our flocks and play, I en-vied not the fair-est dame, Tho ne'er so rich and gay.

Oh, the broom, the bon-nie, bon-nie broom, The _____ broom o' the Cow-den-knowes; I wish_ I_ were wi_ my dear_ swain, Wi his pipe_____ and_____ my ewes.

Verses 1 - 3   D.C.   Verses 4   ewes.

Verses 1 - 3   D.C.   Verse 4

50. THE DEIL'S AWA WI TH' EXCISEMAN

Words by Burns

C.T.D.

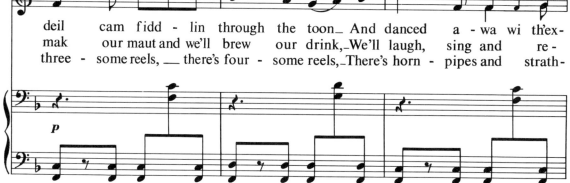

deil cam fidd - lin through the toon— And danced a - wa wi th'ex-
mak our maut and we'll brew our drink,—We'll laugh, sing and re -
three - some reels, — there's four - some reels,—There's horn - pipes and strath-

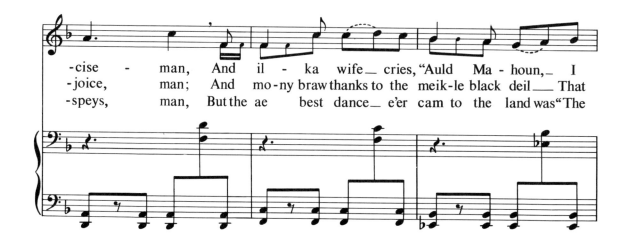

-cise - man, And il - ka wife— cries, "Auld Ma - houn,— I
-joice, man; And mo-ny braw thanks to the meik-le black deil— That
-speys, man, But the ae best dance— e'er cam to the land was "The

51. THE LEA-RIG

Words by Burns

C.T.D.

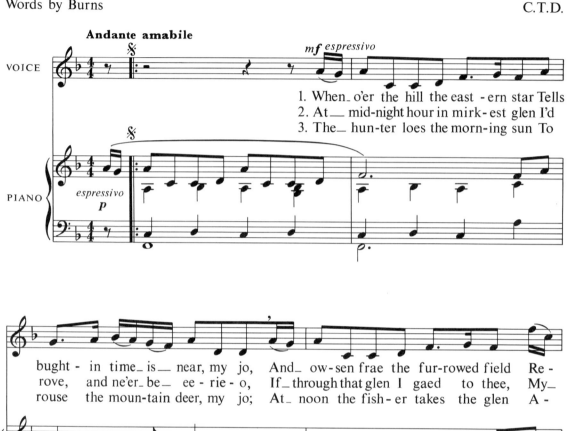

1. When o'er the hill the east-ern star Tells
2. At mid-night hour in mirk-est glen I'd
3. The hun-ter loes the morn-ing sun To

bught - in time is near, my jo, And ow-sen frae the fur-rowed field Re-
rove, and ne'er be ee - rie - o, If through that glen I gaed to thee, My
rouse the moun-tain deer, my jo; At noon the fish - er takes the glen A -

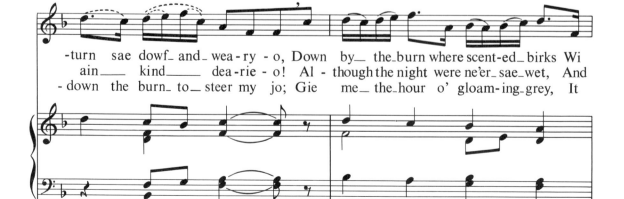

-turn sae dowf and wea - ry - o, Down by the burn where scent-ed birks Wi
ain kind dea - rie - o! Al - though the night were ne'er sae wet, And
-down the burn to steer my jo; Gie me the hour o' gloam-ing grey, It

dew_are_ hang-ing_clear, my jo, I'll_ meet thee on the lea - rig, My_
I_ were_ne'er_sae_ wea - ry - o, I'd_ meet thee on the lea - rig, My_
maks my_ heart sae_chee - ry - o, To_ meet thee on the lea - rig, My_

D.S. after last verse

ain___ kind___ dea - ry - o.
ain___ kind___ dea - ry - o.
ain___ kind___ dea - ry - o.

D.S. after last verse

poco rit.

52. THE LOWLANDS OF HOLLAND

Words anonymous

C.T.D.

Lento moderato (♩=66)

1. The love that I had cho-sen Was to my heart's con-tent, The_ salt sea shall be fro - zen Be - fore that_ I re-pent; Re--pent it will I ne - ver Un - til the day_ I_ dee, Though the low - lands of Hol - land hae twined my love and me.

2. My love lies in the salt sea And I am on the side, E--nough to break a young heart Wha late - ly_was a bride; Wha late - ly was a bon - ny bride, And plea - sure in_ her_ ee; But the low - lands of Hol - land hae twined my love and me.

3. *(optional)* My love he built a braw ship And sent her to the sea, Wi_ se - ven score brave ma - ri - ners To bear her_ com - pa - ny; Three score gaed to the bot - tom And three score died_ at_ sea, And the low - lands of Hol - land hae twined my love and me.

D.C.
vv. 2-3

last verse

4. There shall nae man-tle co-ver me, Nor kame come in my hair, There shall

cantabile

sim.

nei - ther coal nor can - dle-light Come in my_ bo - wer mair; Nor

shall I hae a - ni -ther love Un - til the day_ I_ dee._ I

rit.

ne -ver loved a love but ane And he's drowned in the sea._

53. THE SUN RISES BRIGHT IN FRANCE

Words by
Allan Cunningham

C.T.D.

1. The sun ris-es bright in France, And fair_ sets_ he,_ But he has tint the blink he had In my ain coun-try; It's_ nae my ain_ ru - in That weets_ aye my ee,_ But the dear Ma-rie I left a-hin Wi sweet bairn-ies three, And it's oh! wae's_ me.

2. Fu bein-ly lowed my ain hearth And smiled my ain Ma - rie;— O I hae left my heart be-hind In my ain coun-try. O— I'm leal to hea - ven Which aye was leal to me,——— And it's there I'll meet ye a'— soon Frae my ain coun- -try, And it's oh! wae's— me.

54. THERE ARE TWA BONNY MAIDENS

Words by James Hogg

C.T.D.

1. There are twa bon-ny mai - dens and
2. There is Flo - ra my ho - ney, sae

three bon - ny mai - dens Cam ower the Minch and
dear and sae bon - ny, And ane that's sae tall and sae

cam ower the main, Wi the wind for their way and the
hand - some with - al; Put the ane for my king, and the

cor - ry for their hame, And they are dear - ly wel - come to
i - ther for my queen, And they are dear - ly wel - come to

Skye a - gain. Come a - long, come a - long wi your boa-tie and your song, My_
Skye a - gain. Come a - long, come a - long wi your boa-tie and your song, My_

ain bon-ny mai - dens, my twa bon-ny mai-dens, For the
ain bon-ny mai - dens, my twa bon-ny mai-dens, For the

night it is dark and the red - coat is gone, And ye are dear-ly wel-come to
La - dy Mac-ou - lan, she dwells a' her lane And she'll wel-come you dear-ly to

Skye a - gain.

Skye a - gain!

55. THE WEE COOPER O' FIFE

Words anonymous

C.T.D.

Vivace (♩.=120)

VOICE

1. There was a wee coo-per wha
2. She wad - na bake and she
3. She wad - na card and she

PIANO

p staccato

lived_ in Fife,
wad - na brew,
wad - na spin,

Nick-et-y nack-et-y noo, noo, noo, For the
And
For the

he has got-ten a gen-tle wife,
spoil-ing o' her come-ly hue,
sham-ing o' her gen-tle kin,

Hey Wil-lie Wall-a-chy

ho John Doug-al, A - lane quo Rush-et -y roo, roo, roo!   roo,   roo,

roo! _____

4. The cooper's awa to his woo' pack
        Nickety *etc.*
    And he's laid a sheepskin on his wife's back
        Hey Willie . . . *etc.*

5. "I'll no thrash you for your proud kin,
        Nickety . . .
    But I will thrash my ain sheepskin."
        Hey . . .

6. "O I will bake and I will brew:
        Nickety . . .
    And never think mair o' my comely hue."
        Hey . . .

7. "O I will card and I will spin:
        Nickety . . .
    And never think mair o' my gentle kin."
        Hey . . .

8. A' ye wha hae gotten a gentle wife
        Nickety . . .
    Just send ye for the wee cooper o' Fife.
        Hey . . .

56. THE WHITE COCKADE

Words by Burns

G.C.M.

57. THE WINTER IT IS PAST

Words anonymous
revised by Burns

C.T.D.

58. THE YELLOW-HAIRED LADDIE

Words anonymous

C.T.D.

1. The yel-low-haired lad-die sat on yon burn brae, Cries, "Milk the ewes, las-sie, let nane o' them gae." And aye she milk-it and aye she sang: "The yel-low-haired lad-die shall

2. "The wea-ther is cauld, and my claith-ing is thin, The ewes are new clip-pit, they win-na bucht in. They win-na bucht in, al--though I should dee, O yel-low-haired lad-die, be

3. The guid-wife cries butt the hoose, "Jen-ny, come ben, The cheese is to mak, and the but-ter to kirn." "Though but-ter and cheese and a' should gang sour, I'll crack and kiss wi my love

be   my_ guid - man.
kind   to _____ me."
ae   half - -

ae   half - hour,   and_ we'll_ e'en_ mak_ it_ three, ___   For the

yel - low - haired_ lad - die_ my   hus - band_ shall_ be."

59. WILLIE WASTLE DWALLS ON TWEED

Words by Burns

C.T.D.

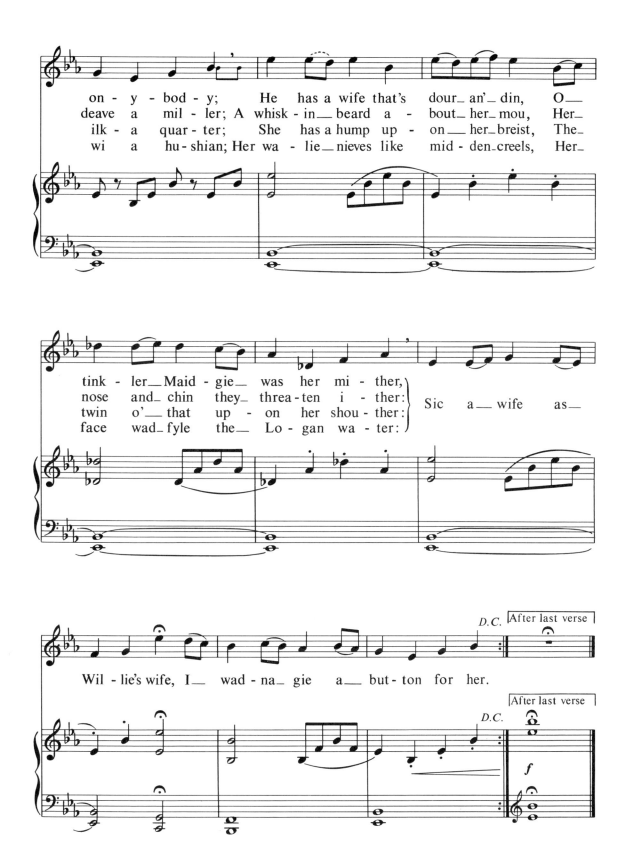

on - y - bod - y; He has a wife that's dour an' din, O__
deave a mil - ler; A whisk-in__beard a - bout__her__mou, Her__
ilk - a quar - ter; She has a hump up - on__her__breist, The__
wi a hu - shian; Her wa - lie__nieves like mid - den__creels, Her__

tink - ler__Maid - gie__was her mi - ther,
nose and__chin they threa-ten i - ther: Sic a__wife as__
twin o'__that up - on her shou-ther:
face wad__fyle the__Lo - gan wa - ter:

Wil - lie's wife, I__ wad - na__gie a__but-ton for her.

D.C. [After last verse]

[After last verse]

D.C.

f

60. YE BANKS AND BRAES O' BONNY DOON

Words by Burns

C.T.D.

Lento espressivo (♪ = 80)

1. Ye banks and braes o' bon-ny Doon, How can_ ye bloom sae
2. hae I strayed by bon-ny Doon_ To see_ the rose_ and

fresh and fair? How can ye chant, ye litt-le birds, And I___sae wea-ry, fu' o'care? Thou'lt
wood-bine twine, And ilk-a bird sang o'_ its love, And fond-ly sae_did I_ o'mine; Wi_

break my heart, thou warb-ling bird_That wan-tons through the flow'r-ing thorn; Thou
light-some heart_ I pu'd a rose_Fu sweet_ up-on_ its thorn-y tree; And

minds me o' de-part-ed joys,_De-part-ed ne-ver to_ re-turn. 2.Aft
my fause lo-ver staw_ my rose,_But ah!_ he left_ the thorn wi me.

Glossary and Index

GLOSSARY

a–adjective; *adv*–adverb; *c*–conjunction;
n–noun; *p*–preposition; *v*–verb.

abeigh	*adv*	– at a distance	daur	*v*	– dare
abuin	*p*	– above	deave	*v*	– deafen
acquent	*a*	– acquainted	deuk dub	*n*	– duck pond
aft	*adv*	– often	dow	*v*	– can
aiken tree	*n*	– oak tree	dowf	*a*	– sad
ajee	*a*	– open	dowie	*a*	– dull
asklent	*adv*	– aslant	drap	*n*	– drop
bannet	*n*	– bonnet	dule	*n*	– sorrow
baudrons	*n*	– cat	dunderpeuks	*n*	– a disease of horses
beld	*a*	– bald	fainness	*n*	– pleasure
bield	*n*	– shelter (home)	fen	*n*	– shift
bienly	*adv*	– cosily	fiercie	*n*	– bad temper
birken	*a*	– made of birch	flee	*n*	– jot
blatherskite	*n*	– blether	fleeched	*v*	– coaxed
blaw	*v*	– blow	fleuk	*v*	– shivers
bleer	*v*	– dim	forpit	*n*	– measure of half a gallon
blin	*a*	– blind			
bluddie	*a*	– bloody	fou	*a*	– full
board-en	*n*	– table-end	frichtet	*a*	– frightened
bogle	*n*	– spectre	fu	*adv*	– full
bow-houghed	*a*	– bow-legged	fyle	*v*	– defile
brent	*a*	– unwrinkled	gabbin	*v*	– talking
breuk	*n*	– boil	gart	*v*	– made
brose	*n*	– a type of porridge	gin	*c*	– if
buchts	*n*	– sheepfolds	glammer	*n*	– spell
buik	*n*	– bench	gleg	*a*	– keen
busk	*v*	– adorn	gowd	*n*	– gold
canty	*a*	– happy	gree	*n*	– first place
carl	*n*	– man	ground o' yer		
cauldrife	*a*	– awkward	trunkie	*n*	– "bottom drawer"
chandler-shaftit	*a*	– lantern-jawed	grunzie	*n*	– face
clamb	*v*	– climbed	guid (gude)	*a*	– good
cleads	*v*	– clothes	hale	*a*	– well (healthy)
cleeks	*n*	– cramp	hallanshaker	*n*	– beggar
clue	*n*	– ball of wool	hand-breed	*n*	– hand's breadth
clyack horn	*n*	– drinking horn	hap	*n*	– wrap
coort	*v*	– court	hawkit	*a*	– white-faced
coost (cuist)	*v*	– cast	hecht	*v*	– promised
crooks	*n*	– crooked spine	heigh	*a or adv*	– high
crouse	*a*	– cheerful	hemp heckle	*n*	– comb for dressing hemp
cut-luggit	*a*	– crop-eared			
daffin	*n*	– flirting	hem-shinned	*a*	– bow-legged

102

heugh	*n*	– crag	preed	*v*	– kissed
hizzie	*n*	– hussy	rantin	*a*	– roistering
howe	*n*	– valley	,, ,,	*v*	– blazing
howks	*n*	– furrows	rowes	*v*	– flows
ilka	*a*	– each	sabbin	*v*	– sobbing
ingle-nook	*n*	– chimney corner	sark	*n*	– shirt
jaud	*n*	– old woman	shouther	*n*	– shoulder
jawpish	*n*	– a disease of horses	shyre	*a*	– complete
kail	*n*	– colewart	skeigh	*a*	– coy
kame	*n*	– comb	smoored	*v*	– smothered
kebbock	*n*	– cheese	snout	*n*	– face
keckle	*v*	– cackle (laugh)	sonsy	*a*	– well-built
knags	*n*	– knobs	spiered (speered)	*v*	– asked
knowe	*n*	– knoll	steel-wamed	*a*	– fat-bellied
laigh	*a or adv*	– low	steer	*v*	– touch
lammie	*n*	– darling	sten	*n*	– leap
lave	*n*	– the remainder	stook	*n*	– stalk
lear	*n*	– knowledge	stounds	*v*	– aches
lee-lang	*a*	– live-long	stowlins	*adv*	– secretly
leesome	*adv*	– calmly	stown	*v*	– stolen
leglin	*n*	– milking-stool	syne	*adv*	– then
lick	*n*	– wag	tent	*n*	– heed
linking	*v*	– hurrying	thripling kame	*n*	– comb for separating the seed of flax
linn	*n*	– waterfall			
lint	*n*	– flax	tint	*v*	– lost
loof	*n*	– palm of the hand	tittie	*n*	– sister
loon	*n*	– rascal	tocher-good	*n*	– dowry
loot	*v*	– bow	toom	*v*	– empty
loup	*v*	– leap	totter	*v*	– walk feebly
lunzie-banes	*n*	– loin bones	tow	*n*	– flax
meikle (mickle, muckle)	*a*	– much	trow	*v*	– believe
midden-creels	*n*	– manure baskets	truffs	*n*	– turfs
minnie	*n*	– mother	twined	*v*	– separated
monkie	*n*	– rope for fastening cattle	unco	*adv*	– very
			walie	*a*	– big
mou	*n*	– mouth	wame	*n*	– stomach
neuks	*n*	– hollows	waukin	*a*	– awake
nieves	*n*	– fists	well-faured	*a*	– well-favoured
owsen	*n*	– oxen	wheezlock	*n*	– short wind
pawky	*a*	– shrewd	wist	*v*	– wished (knew)
plenishin	*n*	– goods	wyle	*v*	– lure
pleugh	*n*	– plough	yett	*n*	– gate
poortith	*n*	– poverty	yeuk	*n*	– itch
pow	*n*	– head	yowes	*n*	– ewes

INDEX

a = suitable for primary (junior) classes; b = suitable for secondary girls' classes; c = suitable for secondary boys' classes; d = suitable for adult female singers; e = suitable for adult male singers.

Title	No.	a	b	c	d	e
O gin I were a baron's heir	31	a		c		e
O gin I were where Gadie rins	32	a	b	c	d	e
O gin my love were yon red rose	35			c		e
Oh where, tell me where	45	a	b		d	
O Kenmure's on and awa	33	a	b	c	d	e
O lay thy loof in mine, lass	34			c		e
O Robin is my only jo	19		b		d	
O this is no' my ain lassie	36	a		c		e
O weel may the boatie row	40	a	b		d	
O whistle and I'll come to ye	41		b		d	
O Willy's rare and Willy's fair	17		b		d	
O Willie was a wanton wag	42		b	c	d	e
Rattlin roarin Willie	37		b		d	
Tam Glen	43		b		d	
The auld man's mare's deid	44	a	b	c	d	e
The birks of Aberfeldy	38	a		c		e
The blue bell of Scotland	45	a	b		d	
The Bob o' Dunblane	21			c		e
The bonny banks of Loch Lomond	47		b	c	d	e
The brisk young lad	48	a	b		d	
The broom o' the Cowdenknowes	49	a	b		d	
The deil's awa wi th' exciseman	50	a	b	c	d	e
The flowers o' the forest	29		b		d	e
The gipsies cam tae our lord's yett	18		b	c	d	e
The lea-rig	51		b	c	d	e
The love that I had chosen	52		b		d	
The lowlands of Holland	52		b		d	
The queen's Maries	46	a	b		d	
There are twa bonny maidens	54	a		c		e
There cam a young man	48	a	b		d	
There lived a man in oor toon	3	a	b	c		
The sun rises bright in France	53			c		e
The wee cooper o' Fife	55	a	b	c	d	e
The white cockade	56	a	b		d	
The winter it is past	57		b		d	
The yellow-haired laddie	58		b		d	
Wee Willie Gray	39	a	b		d	e
Wha wadna be in love	23	a		c		e
When o'er the hill the eastern star	51		b	c	d	e
Where hae ye been a' day	25		b		d	
Willie Wastle dwalls on Tweed	59		b	c	d	e
Ye banks and braes	60		b		d	
Yestreen the queen had four Maries	46	a	b		d	

The Hardie Press